About the Author

Chrissie Daplyn was born in Chesterfield towards the end of WWII, her mother and sisters having been evacuated there from East Anglia. At the end of the war they returned home to Lowestoft where she has lived ever since.

A practising Christian since the age of twelve, she acquired the habit of writing a journal and it seemed natural to begin writing down what was happening as her health deteriorated and she endured numerous hospital admissions and surgery.

Together with her husband of 43 years, Chrissie has worked in her local church which is affiliated to New Frontiers, a worldwide family of evangelical churches committed to preaching the gospel of Jesus Christ and bringing hope and healing to all people. Together they have encountered the whole range of people's problems and difficulties and have endeavoured to be of service and help to their congregations. She has been a member of King's Church, Great Yarmouth which was established in 1995 and which is a planted-out church from Lowestoft Community Church which her husband, along with others, founded in 1985.

Among her various administrative posts in her employment Chrissie worked for her Local Authority for several years in their Social Services Department, initially for a generic social work team and as co-ordinator for their Child Protection Team. Now officially retired, Chrissie continues to assist Brian in running their small picture framing business.

ONE IN A MILLION

By

CHRISSIE DAPLYN

Published by

MELROSE BOOKS

An Imprint of Melrose Press Limited
St Thomas Place, Ely
Cambridgeshire
CB7 4GG, UK
www.melrosebooks.com

FIRST EDITION

Copyright © Chrissie Daplyn 2007

The Author asserts her moral right to
be identified as the author of this work

Cover designed by Nikki Bovis-Coulter, 2Fish Productions

ISBN 978 1 906050 10 8

All rights reserved. No part of this publication may be reproduced, stored in a retrieval system, or transmitted, in any form or by any means electronic, mechanical , photocopying, recording or otherwise, without the prior permission of the publishers.

This book is sold subject to the condition that it shall not, by way of trade or otherwise, be lent, re-sold, hired out or otherwise circulated without the publisher's prior consent in any form of binding or cover other than that in which it is published and without a similar condition including this condition being imposed on the subsequent purchaser.

Printed and bound in Great Britain by:
CPI Antony Rowe, Bumpers Farm,
Chippenham, Wiltshire, SN14 6LH, UK

Table of Contents

ACKNOWLEDGEMENTS

"It is difficult to express my gratitude fully to everyone who contributed to my life and comfort during my illness and eventual recovery.

My thanks, of course, to the staff at The North Hampshire Hospital, Basingstoke whose medical skill gave me more years on this planet.

Unending thanks to my husband and family who loved me and cared for me and didn't mind that I disrupted their lives.

To the countless people who prayed to God for my healing believing in faith that He would hear and answer.

He did - and to Him I am most grateful!"

INTRODUCTION

I usually find the *Introduction* or *Preface* to any book that I am reading rather an irritation, as I am eager to get going on the main chapters. I commend you for overcoming any impatience you may have to start on the main chapters.

This book is a brief account of what happened to me – and my husband – and how we battled through confusion and heartbreak.

The reason for the title 'One in a Million' is because this was part of the medical description of the condition with which I was diagnosed.

My medical condition was extremely unusual, but my story is littered with the *usual,* so I hope, therefore, that you can identify with some of the everyday things I have mentioned.

Writing down what has happened to me has been very therapeutic, but more than that, I wanted to give thanks to God for His amazing grace and mercy upon my life.

Oswald Chambers says that Christians should be able to look the darkest, blackest fact full in the face without damaging God's character. Our inclination is to blame God when things appear to be going wrong for us. If this inclination has crept upon me in my lowest moments it has soon been dispelled by His great and mighty promises.

As well as having to rely on the love and goodness of an invisible God, my very visible husband, Brian, has been my constant source of love, support and optimism. His goodness and sense of humour has brought sunshine into some very gloomy days.

I hope my story will both interest you and challenge you.

1

THE AWFUL TRUTH

I pulled the old medical book from the bookcase. It was the only medical book I possessed. It had been given to me by an elderly neighbour who we had helped to move house. The letter in my hand was from my local hospital as I frantically thumbed through the old tome of 'Women's Diseases'.

It was Spring 2001 and I was just out of hospital for the second time with this particular illness. In fact, I had had five different lots of surgery, mostly for gynaecological problems, but this last operation had been shocking for me. Three years previously, in 1998, I had a very large ovarian cyst removed with the ovaries. (I had a hysterectomy several years previous to this.) The consultant had said at the time that the cyst had ruptured by the time they removed it, so I was to keep an eye on myself because "these things have a habit of returning". Despite my request for a regular ultrasound, the GP was adamant that it would be best for me to monitor myself. No-one made much fuss about what had happened to me, so I got on with my life.

In January 2001 I discovered another lump in my left side. I was aware that I had been getting fat but you expect to *spread* a little when you get past 50! The GP referred me directly and I was soon in the gynaecological clinic again. I would need to be admitted again and "I may need to refer you to my colleague in Norfolk" the consultant informed me as he continued to write in my file without looking at me. Of course, I knew his reference to "my colleague" was the oncologist in the nearby city hospital. I waited for my bed and was admitted in March 2001. When I woke up from the surgery they had removed the mass but had had to repair my colon and had given me a temporary colostomy. The consultant leaned on my bed as I drowsily looked at him. "I am afraid there will be more surgery," he said with some degree of sympathy in his voice. They assured me that the mass had not been malignant but all the same it sounded serious. All I could think of at that time was that the colostomy was temporary and I could have it reversed.

So began my quest for information. As soon as I got home from the hospital I wrote to my consultant to ask the precise name of the cyst/mass which he had removed. His reply – which I was now holding in my hand – was one sentence and read thus: "Further to your enquiry, the condition you had is Pseudomyxoma Peritonei".

The old medical book smelled musty and the pages were brown with age. It took me a while to find the explanation for Pseudomyxoma Peritonei but the words stood out with glaring clarity; "and since it is impossible to remove the implants it usually proves fatal".

I was 57 years old. I had been a practicing Christian since I was twelve years old and my husband Brian had been in church leadership for nearly twenty years. I had already been through so much with my health, had never been able to have children, and here I was trying to come to terms with my *fatal* condition. I'm sure everyone who faces very serious health issues feels the same – *this happens to other people not to me.*

The medical book was old, of course it was, so I held on to the hope that in this enlightened medical age there was a better prognosis for me. It may have been an old book but it was certainly not out of date as far as its summary of my condition was concerned. A nurse friend searched the internet and came to see me with great kindness and sympathy. What I had was very rare and there was no definitive treatment except continued surgery which would eventually become life threatening.

Pseudomyxoma Peritonei is a rare disease of the abdominal or peritoneal cavity. The majority of cases result from a ruptured mucus secreting adenoma of the appendix. Sometimes it can arise in other organs but this is rare. Large amounts of jelly-like mucinous fluid grow and spread on the peritoneum which lines the abdominal cavity. It is estimated that it occurs in one in a million people each year. It can occur in men as well as women. These mucinous implants/cells continue to grow and increase, causing abdominal distension, and eventually compress other organs. The disease is considered to be "borderline malignant" but it does not spread via the lymphatic system or by the blood vessels; it spreads only within the abdominal cavity. The hospital told me there was no treatment – meaning that the normal radiotherapy and chemotherapy was not an option.

So there it was! This deadly *thing* growing inside me would keep on growing and the only option was to keep having surgery. It was difficult to explain to people what was wrong with me – their comments would always be "Well I've never heard of that before". Each time I had to repeat the horrible tale it made me more pessimistic about my chances of staying alive.

I had loved God since I was twelve years old and I was sure of God's sovereignty and His permissive will, but I was still dismayed at what the future held for me. Brian and I decided to tackle it on two fronts. We had to believe in God for a miracle and at the same time ascertain if there was any research being done that would afford me some medical help.

2

FAMILY JOTTINGS

As I write about some of our family history I know I run the risk of being tedious – it's like looking at other people's holiday photographs. However, there are some interesting events in both our families that will give you a cameo picture of both Brian and myself.

I was conceived during the Second World War – and that nearly didn't happen as my father was one of thousands of men who were rescued from the beaches of Dunkirk in 1940. He was in the sea for many long hours before a small boat picked him up and brought him back over the English Channel. My mother always said he was a "nice man" before he went into the Army where he learned to smoke and drink and show off. Maybe it was the trauma of war that altered him. Whilst my mother was pregnant with me and my father was away serving with his regiment, she remained initially living in Lowestoft with my two sisters who were six and four at the time. Lowestoft is a lovely town nestling on the most easterly edge of East Anglia. It was bombarded cruelly during those difficult war years. German bombers, on their way home, would sometimes drop their last load before heading out across the North Sea. One day a German bomb landed on the front door step of my mother's small terraced house which she rented. The bomb caused an enormous crater but did not explode. Soon afterwards my mother and her small family were evacuated to Whitwell, Chesterfield, where I was born on 6th August 1944. My mother was very ill whilst giving birth to me and prayed that God would spare us both. He did, and so she called me Christine in thankfulness. Despite the might of the German Luftwaffe and the frailty of my mother's health, I arrived, watched over by a God who intended that I should live and know Him.

When the war ended in 1945 and my father was demobbed we were re-housed back in Lowestoft in one of those now famous 'prefabs'. For all young readers who have no idea of what a prefab was, I can only describe it as a corrugated bungalow, prefabricated and bolted together on site for speedy, much needed housing as the men came home from the war. I remember cold winters in this prefab and cold linoleum floors. Of course, everyone thought they were wonderful at the time. I also remember a large aggressive pet cat that used to guard the toilet and attack my small legs as I came out. I remember lots of fun with my sisters and their friends. We had little in the way of toys but we would put on musical shows – dressing up and singing and dancing. We charged half an old penny to other children to come and watch and we threw in a free glass of lemonade – made with lemonade crystals.

My father went to work in the large shipyards in Lowestoft and had secure employment up until his retirement. We eventually moved into a brand new three-bedroom house on a new council estate. Number 45 Europa Road was where my sisters and I grew up and dreamed our dreams of boyfriends and weddings, and all things wonderful.

God has a plan and a purpose to draw men and women to himself. He will tenaciously pursue those plans in order for us to become aware of Him. Even when we are completely ignorant of His love and calling upon our lives, He watches over His Word for our ultimate salvation. A large Baptist church in Lowestoft had seen the sprawling need of the council estate where we lived and had set up a little mission church on a plot of land just a few roads from where we lived. My friend next door took me to Sunday School and I immediately felt I belonged with these people. I was always a sensitive soul and hated roughness and loudness. My Sunday School teachers were kind and nice and I loved them. Sunday services were always facilitated by visiting speakers because there was no resident pastor. I started going to the services and took my sister along. How excited we were to hear that the Americans from the nearby Air Force Base were coming to hold some evangelistic meetings. They were *so beautiful* – but also so challenging as they preached the gospel. My sister Rita, who was four years older than me, gave her life to Jesus. She was sixteen and quite the 'good time' girl. Her life changed dramatically and she has never stopped loving the Lord who intervened in her life that night. A few nights later I, too, was prayed with and became a Christian at the age of twelve. It was November and the streets were dark as I walked home alone. I don't remember why my sister was not with me but I do remember that the Holy Spirit confirmed deep in my heart that I was now a child of God. My eldest sister, Jackie, made a decision to follow the Christian pathway but soon went off to live her life in a different kind of way. I am happy that today she has regained her faith in God.

Rita and I each married Christian guys who were good friends. We served God and worshipped at this Baptist church for many years. I have lovely memories of long summer days when we organised Sunday School outings for the children.

My mother died in 1986 and went to be with the Lord. Her story would make a very readable 'Catherine Cookson' type book. She was one of three children born to an unmarried woman in the early years of the twentieth century. In today's society it would be tolerated but in those days it was shame and disgrace. My mother was the eldest of three; she had a brother and a younger sister. Their mother, my grandmother, died of tuberculosis at the age of twenty-eight years, leaving them at the mercy of an unkind world. My mother's grandfather, whose first wife had died, married again and took the three children in, expecting his young wife to care for them. His eventual death secured for the children an uncertain future of unhappiness and insecurity. My mother would recall times when kind neighbours and shopkeepers would give them biscuits and pieces of bread.

My mother's brother, Uncle Jack, joined the Navy and spent time overseas. In January 1948 he deserted from the Navy and went missing. As the years went by my mother made several attempts to find him but to no avail. This was always a source of grief to her that she would not see him again. A letter from the naval welfare officer dated November 1950 indicates that his last known address was in Newport, Monmouthshire. My mother died without knowing what happened to him. My mother's younger sister married a local man and appeared happy until she died in 1991.

My father had been a heavy smoker and suffered many health problems because of it. Each operation he had brought renewed resolve to give up but it was not long before he was smoking again and pretending that he wasn't. He kept an open Coke can on his table so that if we visited unexpectedly he could pop the cigarette into the can. It was very funny because he had no explanation for his discoloured yellowing ceilings and walls and the cloud of smoke disappearing out of the open window, to say nothing of the smell of smoke which we were all aware of. During his last days he allowed us to pray with him but we were never sure if he found forgiveness and peace with Jesus before he died. Quite recently the Lord graciously gave me a dream about him and I'm now sure that he is in heaven.

Brian's family history is less eventful but nevertheless touched by God's amazing grace. His father was a master baker owning his own business, so that during the war he was engaged in the business at home of feeding the nation. He was a gambling man who entertained 'card schools' in his home and made regular visits to the local greyhound race course. He was very successful and won large amounts of money over the years. Brian had one older sister who became a Christian through the work and preaching of the Faith Mission. She took Brian's mother along to hear the gospel being preached and she too gave her life to Jesus. Their prayers were unceasing for their father and husband and eventually he went along to some of the meetings with his family. After hearing the gospel preached on several occasions and resisting the conviction of the Holy Spirit over several weeks, he found himself falling to his knees one day when he was alone in his bake house. He begged God to forgive him and have mercy on his wicked ways. That day, without a preacher in sight, he got up off his knees a changed man. God had opened the eyes of his heart to reveal his need to repent. He chiselled a cross into the concrete floor of his bake house to remind him each day of the mercy and kindness of God. He never returned to his gambling habits but became a devoted servant of God, readily witnessing to people until his death. Brian became a committed Christian a few months after seeing how God's love had touched his father. Brian's family were all baptised and attended the Baptist church in Lowestoft. It was this particular church which had established the little mission on the council estate where I grew up. Brian's mother was one of the women who taught me in Sunday School and that is how I got to know the family and fall in love with their son.

I am continually amazed at God's mercy and grace to people. I constantly wonder at His grace upon our families. My family were 'nobodies', with nothing to recommend us, but God made sure that out of all the chaos His grace and His wonderful love touched and changed our lives for all eternity. It takes my breath away even as I think about it today.

This is how Brian and I met and married and began to serve God in the local church. We have had to move churches over the years as we embraced a more charismatic style of worshipping when the Holy Spirit moved powerfully throughout many denominations. Brian has now been involved in church leadership for more than twenty-five years and we are currently serving a 'planted out' church just over the border in Norfolk.

And this is where we came in – so to speak – when my health failed. "But the Lord stood with us", as you will see.

3

GOD'S REMA WORD

In the early weeks of 1998, I was sitting at home waiting to be admitted to hospital for the removal of the ovarian cyst. I had no idea at that time that this was something much more sinister. Nevertheless, I was nervous and scared about the surgery. I had been reading Psalm 91 "For He will command His angels concerning you to guard you in all your ways, they will lift you up in their hands, so that you will not strike your foot against a stone" (vs. 11 & 12). I said to God "This is all very wonderful but how can I know that I can claim this promise from your word for myself today". Within five minutes of my prayer, the telephone rang and I heard the familiar voice of a dear Christian friend. She said "Chrissie, I have just been praying for you and I felt the Lord give me this Scripture for you – Psalm 91 verses 11 and 12!". At the very moment I was asking God to confirm His word for me, the Holy Spirit was laying that very word on my friend's heart.

During 1999, my journal indicates that we were all praying for the crisis in Kosovo. It was during 1999 that I felt the Holy Spirit give me four particular words for my life. One of those words was "… the Best Man". Not very meaningful and certainly bearing no connection to anything in my life at that time. The four statements God had given me seemed unconnected and bizarre but I entered them in my journal and forgot about them for many months. "The Best Man" came to have such significance in my life and I will tell you about that later.

The new millennium came in and with it more words from God to me. In October 2000 I heard the word 'tsunami' for the first time in my life. Why this word had never found a place in my knowledge I do not know, but I heard and read it again and again and began to think God was saying something to me. Of course, as I write this, the word tsunami is known to everyone in the world now since the Boxing Day disaster in 2004 in South East Asia. Tsunami is Japanese for large wave, so I began to ask the Lord what he was saying to me. Many times I switched on the television I heard the word and viewed the pictures of the destructive power of these mega waves. I sat in church a couple of weeks later and prayed that if this was a word from God, He would speak again. A man in our fellowship got up and began to talk about tsunamis saying that God was going to shake foundations and old securities would crumble as He touched us with a mighty wave of His power. I believed that this prophetic word was for our church corporately but also for me as an individual.

In November 2000 I had a dream that I was sure had a potent meaning for me. I dream a lot, and I know that some are just a jumble of leftover thoughts and feelings but this particular dream stayed with me into the next day as I felt the Holy Spirit confirming something to me. I dreamed that I was standing across the street looking at our bungalow and I could see fire smouldering throughout the length of the foundations. I knew the fire had taken hold and once ignited would burn up everything we owned. In my dream I telephoned for the Fire Brigade but they said they couldn't come and no help was available. I remember the sheer panic in my spirit as I knew I was about to lose all my security and comfortableness.

Glad to wake up – as you are when stuck in a nightmare – I tried to forget the dream, but I knew the Holy Spirit had warned me and prepared me for what God was about to do in my life. Home represents for me familiarity, security and safety, a place where chaos and dismay and change are kept at bay. Whatever happened in our ministry, we could always find a safe refuge at home. I now know that God was telling me again that He was about to invade the 'safe' place of my way of life. All my securities were about to be challenged. The usual help would not be available for me and I would have to believe in Him alone for His help.

The tsunami hit me the following year as the circumstances swept over our lives. All my old securities were burned up as the hot fires of adversity broke over us.

4

'FLAWLESS FATHER'

The new year is always full of hope and good resolutions to be a better Christian and do more for the Kingdom of God. I was soaking in a lovely warm bath one January evening in 2001 when I felt the large lump in my left side. I remember groaning audibly "Oh no – not again". I had to wait over a week to get an appointment with the GP and he confirmed my worst fears. There was another growth and I would need further surgery.

Another two weeks went by before I was able to see the gynaecologist at the local hospital. He was his usual 'professional' self without much to say. He told me I would be given an admission date for another laparotomy to remove the lump and if need be I would be referred to an oncologist.

I could not believe that I had to go through this again. Little did I know that what I was about to face would only be a dress rehearsal for the next year. I needed encouragement and hope and God, as usual, spoke again and again through His Word and various other means in order to reassure me.

Some quotes in my diary just before going into hospital that year indicate how the Holy Spirit was sustaining me. "Infinite wisdom has arranged the whole with infinite love, and infinite power enables me to rest upon that love. I am in the dear Father's hands – all is secure. When I look to Him, I see nothing but faithfulness and immutability and truth, and I have the sweetest peace" (Charles Simeon 1792–1836 as he was dying).

A few days before going into hospital, God gave me Psalm 18 v. 30 "As for God His way is perfect, the Word of the Lord is flawless". I had to believe that in spite of the difficulties our Father in heaven never makes a mistake. His dealings with us are completely flawless and what He permits in our lives is without error.

Brian took me into hospital at the end of March and when we arrived on the ward there were no beds immediately available. Myself and about three other women were asked to wait in the day room. As we passed a single side room, a nurse was saying to a new patient – "but you completed the form for an amenity bed". "Well I misunderstood, I cannot pay for this room" was the poor lady's reply. This poor woman eventually turned up in the day room to wait like the rest of us for a bed on the main ward. The sister on the gynaecology ward was a Christian who I knew; in fact she had been a staff nurse on the ward during my last lot of surgery. Unknown to me, the ward staff were trying to juggle the bed crisis created by the woman who had booked a private room and then said she couldn't pay for it. The staff told me afterwards that they decided to give me the private room because *I was nice and Sister knew me!* A nurse popped her head around the door and called my name and I was given the private room. Although I was initially disappointed to be all on my own, it turned out to be God's gracious provision for me.

I was the last on the consultant's operating list that day; I guess he knew I might be a problem. I had the statutory bath and got into the operating gown but I felt dreadful; my throat was sore and I knew I was nursing an infection. My temperature was normal so they paid little attention to how odd I felt. They probably thought it was pre-op nerves. It turned out that I did have a throat infection which made my recovery after surgery all the more difficult. The pre-med tablets kicked in and I went to sleep without being conscious of being wheeled down to theatre.

I woke up in the middle of the night, I was alone and it was very dark apart from a dim light coming through the slightly open door. Someone had told me I had a colostomy but I didn't remember being told although my brain had the information and quickly told me so. I was very scared and rang the bell for the nurse. She was a kind, sweet-natured girl who bathed my parched lips and tongue. Yes, she confirmed, they had had to give me a colostomy. (A stoma opening onto the surface of the belly where waste is collected instead of the normal opening of the bowels). I was drowsy but devastated and I cried as she knelt by my bed and held my hand. I asked her if she ever prayed and she said she used to but had not done so for a long time. The senior staff nurse came in to assess me and said that she had been reading my notes and it looked like the stoma was only temporary and could be reversed. It was something.

Brian had visited the hospital at seven in the evening but I was still in the recovery room but they told him that the consultant wanted to see him. He eventually saw me but I was unaware of his kiss on my face. He didn't sleep much that night.

Hospital doctors arrive like buses – all at once! My consultant arrived the next morning with his entourage of juniors and nurses. He explained the cystic mass had been attached to the wall of my bowel and he had had to call in a general surgeon to repair the colon. "We thought it wise to allow the colon time to heal that is why you have a colostomy, but it is reversible". I remember getting hold of the lapel on his jacket and saying *thank you, thank you!* However, his next comment was not so encouraging: "I'm afraid there will be more surgery". They had just opened me up and supposedly fixed me – why would there be more? At that very moment the general on-call surgeon bounced into my room. He shook my hand, beamed down at me, introduced himself by name and told me that he was the consultant who had been called in to repair my colon. "Don't be alarmed," he continued, "we can soon put you back together again." He was like a breath of fresh air; very positive and giving orders about my medication. "We will soon get that reversed in no time at all," he said, pointing to where the bag was situated on my belly. He smiled at me as he left the room but within a minute his face was at the door again: "Oh, I forgot to tell you, I removed your appendix also, it was full of the same material". I was later to learn how significant this was.

The private room proved to be a peaceful haven for my three-week stay. It afforded me rest and quiet away from the busy ward and gave me privacy getting used to changing my stoma dressing. Eventually I got used to the idea of having a colostomy but I could not get used to the necessity for *more surgery*. An Egyptian registrar was very kind and spent time with us saying that the 'trick' was knowing when to operate next. Our limited knowledge of the disease left us confused and depressed. However, I determined that I must focus on recovering from *this* surgery and try to put the next surgery on the back burner.

I have always loved Amy Carmichael's writings and during those three weeks I read some of her devotional readings. In *'Rose from Brier'*, she says that God chooses our inheritance for us; and writes "I remember with what delight I learned one day that the verb to 'choose', which is used in this Psalm, is the same that is used to describe David choosing, out of all the possible stones in the brook, the five best suited for his purpose. It occurred to me that our heavenly David, our Beloved, chooses out of all possible circumstances – and they are all at his command – those best suited to fulfil His purpose for my life."

It was hard to accept that God had chosen these circumstances for me but I knew that if I could embrace this truth it would bring peace to my soul. I eventually told my heavenly father that I would have chosen differently but that I believed in His goodness and His purpose for my life. It brought me some measure of peace and I tried to resist thinking too far ahead. God had given me Psalm 18 v. 30 before going into hospital but I struggled with the truth that He was flawless in all his dealings with us. I wanted my faith to stand the test but it was hard going.

Christian friends prayed and sent cards and flowers and teddy bears. One night, staff nurse said "You're quite well known aren't you. My friend's mother says her church has been praying for you."

Eventually I was able to return home to convalesce. At least I was nice and slim again and it was lovely to wear fashionable clothes, even though I was conscious all the time of the stoma dressing underneath.

5

Reassurance and Reversal

In June 2001, God spoke very definitely to me using four different people, but each time He said the same thing. We have some dear Christian friends who left Lowestoft and moved to the Isle of Sky. They sent me a tape from The Highlands Conventions entitled *'Taking the Limits off Yourself'*. The sermon was about the Word of the Lord and its mighty dynamic effect in us when we choose to believe God and stop limiting His work in us. The preacher said that when Lazarus died it was not a full stop in his life – just a comma, before Jesus came with His word of life! Treat weakness in life as a pause and believe God will push the button again, he said. We needed to agree with God's

Word and mix our faith with what He has said. He pointed out that before I was a dot on the face of the earth, God had settled the details of my life. When the angel Gabriel visited Mary and told her that she would be the mother of the Son of God, although she didn't understand, she said *Be it unto me as the Lord has said.* She mixed her faith with the Word of God. I felt this sermon was just for me and it made me begin to want to believe God's declaration over my life instead of living under the diagnosis that I had been given.

A few days later I received a letter from another Christian friend who lives in Hamilton, Canada. She sent me a little booklet in which the author spoke of affirming God's Word over our lives and bodies. The booklet said that we needed to mix faith with God's Word by speaking it out of our mouth. This was a means of applying God's medicine and I knew this was another undeniable message and encouragement for me to believe God.

The third and same word came from one of the elders in our church who gave me Matthew 9 verses 20–22 saying he felt the story of the woman who touched Jesus' garment for healing was for me. This Biblical story is of a woman who had been haemorrhaging for twelve years and had spent all her money on trying to find a cure. In desperation she found Jesus one day and crept up behind him in the crowd. Believing she would not be seen in the crowd that thronged around Him, she bent down and touched the hem of His garment. Immediately she knew she had been healed. I thanked the elder without getting too excited about this very familiar story.

A few days later I was reading the *'Summer Bulletin of Christian Witness to Israel'*. John Ross, the then general secretary, had written an article entitled *'Faith Hanging By A Thread'*. He commented on the story in Matthew chapter nine saying "Nervously creeping through the crowd, a sick woman made contact with Jesus by touching the hem, or fringe of his robe. This fringe and what it signified casts an interesting side-light on the Jewishness of Jesus. In the Law (Numbers 15 verses 37–41) the Lord commanded Israel to make tassels on the corners of their garments to remind them of all the commandments of the Lord. Evidently Jesus wore such a fringed garment... It is interesting that in Matthew's story the sick woman believed her needs could be met by making contact with the Lord through that which symbolised Scripture."

This, for me, threw a whole new light upon what the elder had given me. Once again I felt God was saying that His Word could play a vital role in my healing if I would put my faith in what He had said.

One night I had gone to bed early depressed at the thought of this "thing" that was growing again in my abdomen like some sinister alien taking over territory. I was very tearful and said to the Lord that I needed Him to say something about this dreadful condition that I had. Immediately the Holy Spirit dropped into my heart and mind the Scripture "Greater is He that is in you, than He that is in the world". (1 John 4 v. 4). What encouragement! My God was far greater than anything – even this ever increasing Pseudomyxoma mass.

I believe that each one of these words from God was saying the same thing. They had come internationally, nationally, locally and personally. I took them as a word from heaven and began to mix my faith with God's Word, believing that He was greater than any declared diagnosis over my life. This did not mean that I was in denial, as we continued to push for any medical help, but I knew without a doubt that God had spoken to me.

In June 2001, the day before I was admitted to hospital for the reversal of the colostomy, I had an ultrasound and saw the gynaecologist. I could see the tumours on the scan screen, they were approximately one inch and one and a half inches respectively. It didn't seem much to worry about and I felt quite recovered from the surgery by this time. The next day I went into the now familiar local hospital but this time I was on the general surgical ward. It was an interesting place for me as, unlike the gynaecological ward, there were all kinds of different patient conditions.

I did the usual settling in saying hello to the other women in the six-bed bay and finding out what they had been admitted for. I was soon coming round from the anaesthetic, wanting to pass urine but couldn't. A very young male nurse brought me a commode and I was soon able to feel more comfortable, even though a little embarrassed. The process is to start off on fluids then progress to jelly and ice cream, after that a light diet, and as soon as the digestive system works normally, the patient can go home. All of this took a few days and each morning the consultant would arrive to ask if "I had been yet"! It was most embarrassing but I guess the consultants get used to it. Eventually I did go to the toilet normally with a little help from medication. Unfortunately my closure wound became infected. In fact I had picked up the dreaded MRSA super bug.

Rose was an elderly lady who lay in the bed just opposite me. She had been admitted for a very bad abscess on her bowel. She was very interesting to talk to as her husband had been in the army in India where she had lived for many years. We talked about Christianity and she was certainly of the old school who 'believed' in God and knew how to respect the Bible. She had been particularly poorly one day and during the evening I thought she was near to eternity so I lay in bed praying for her soul. At about ten o'clock, the lights were turned out with only the dim night light burning. A woman who had been operated on that day for haemorrhoids could not sit or lay comfortably and she was constantly in and out of bed. She decided she wanted to go to the toilet and walked in the most bizarre way across the ward with her hospital gown billowing out around her. Even to me she looked ghostly in the dim light. She stopped at Rose's bed wondering which way to go. Rose, who had been in a deep deathly sleep, woke up at the very moment this *spectra from another world* paused at the foot of her bed. "Oh are you Jesus?" Rose asked as the woman continued her ethereal journey. Staff nurse came about ten thirty with the drugs trolley and woke Rose up again to give her the medication. "Oh are you an angel?" asked Rose, then she sat up and pointed across at me. "She's a good person," she said with definite persuasion. I knew that my prayers were having an effect on Rose's spirit as she hovered between life and death. Rose recovered enough to make it home for a few months before she died. I hope she is in heaven so that we can talk together again some day.

I, too, made it home after a week but the MRSA bug made me ill and the wound took several weeks to heal even with the district nurse visiting regularly to clean and dress the wound. Life returned to some semblance of normality but we knew the tumours were still growing like some monster inside me.

And then came September 11th with all its horrible chaos for America and the rest of the world, driving from all our minds our own problems and difficulties for a while.

6

London

When I was first diagnosed with Pseudomyxoma Peritonei, we asked the GP and the consultant if they knew of anyone in the country who was treating this condition. We had no response from either. A neighbour was very eager to help. Her son lived in Manchester and among his many '30-something' friends was an oncologist who was about to visit the United States to lecture. My neighbour gave her the details of my condition and she agreed to find out what she could. At the close of one of her lectures she asked, from the platform, if anyone had any information on the treatment of Pseudomyxoma Peritonei. She had several responses and one name came up again and again. Their information indicated that Professor John Shepherd at The Royal Marsden Hospital had been helping people with my condition. I shall be eternally grateful to these people for their interest in me because this piece of information was about to make my future more hopeful.

My neighbour gave me this information towards the end of 2001 and on 27th February 2002 I wrote to my GP requesting a referral to Professor Shepherd. Five weeks passed and I had heard nothing so I decided to pop in and see the G.P. Unfortunately there had been some confusion and the doctor had no recollection of receiving my letter. However, he said he would make the referral straight away. Time was ticking away but I felt I had to trust God. My appointment at The Royal Marsden Hospital eventually came through for 30th April 2002 at 12.30 p.m.

It was 11.00 a.m. and we were stuck in gridlock traffic and had got only as far as Stratford with no hope of getting to South Kensington in time for my 12.30 p.m. appointment. A friend and his wife had agreed to drive us because he was an experienced driver who knew his way around London. We had started out from home at about 6.00 a.m. but an accident on one of the bridges had brought us to a standstill. I was totally reliant on others and could only sit and keep myself from panicking. I remember saying "Well if I miss the appointment it's not the end of the world". My voice sounded calm but inside I was not calm at all. I was also coping with a full bladder and no hope of finding loos in the complete chaos. We decided to park the car and get a train into central London but this alone took another forty-five minutes. I telephoned the hospital on my mobile phone saying I would be late because of the traffic and I was coming on the train. They sympathised with me and said to get there when I could. We caught the westbound underground train to South Kensington and I began to relax.

It was pouring with rain as we walked the short distance to The Royal Marsden Hospital. In the reception waiting room we tried our best to look dignified as we found space for our dripping umbrellas and jackets. I was not in the consulting room long before Professor Shepherd came in saying "You only just caught me, I was going, they said you had telephoned in to cancel". My clarification of the circumstances sounded limp and he was eager to get on with the consultation. He was quite different to how I imagined him and I watched this clever man as he made notes whilst I gave him a brief history. The letter from my surgery had not been very comprehensive so I had to fill in some of the gaps. He examined me then left the room whilst I got myself dressed and composed. He returned a few minutes later, pulled up a chair and faced me with the words "I can't help you, but I know a man who can!" "His name is Brendan Moran," he continued, still giving me direct eye contact "he's Irish but don't hold that against him" – he smiled at his own humour. I later discovered that they were colleagues so this familiar jest was quite acceptable. "Mr. Moran has a special unit in Basingstoke

Hospital and I've nearly finished the letter of referral to him regarding you." Indeed I could see his dictaphone in his hand as he sat explaining things to us. "The operation which Mr. Moran does is risky but you are still fairly young and apart from this current condition which you have, you are fairly fit." He continued explaining about the procedure, how each organ is stripped down of the Psuedo deposits and chemotherapy is administered directly into the abdominal cavity. He was saying that the average operating time is eight to twelve hours, but by this time my mind had ceased to absorb the details. He had given me hope but what a dreadful prospect. "I strongly urge you to think very, very seriously about going for this operation," he said as he leaned towards me in his chair to emphasise his advice. We talked some more and I thanked him for seeing me. He shook my hand, turned to Brian, wished us well and was soon gone, disappearing into his busy life. I never saw him again.

I was in need of tea and comfort by this time, so our friends joined us in the waiting room where we were grateful for the WRVS service. Tea and sandwiches soon warmed us up and we made our way out into the rainy streets of London and back to South Kensington station. I was glad to be going home after such a stressful and uncomfortable day. How close I had come to missing my appointment with this man who knew exactly where I could get help.

7

The Best Man

During May 2002 a letter arrived from Mr. Moran saying he had received Professor Shepherd's referral and arrangements would be made for me to have an overnight stay in Basingstoke Hospital where I would have a CT scan and an assessment and be seen by Mr. Moran. The appointment subsequently came through for 5th and 6th August. By this time I was again getting fatter and the tumour in my pelvis was beginning to show and cause me discomfort. I made frequent visits to the loo because of the pressure on my bladder.

I got out of bed one morning with an overwhelming feeling that the Holy Spirit was speaking to me in my spirit in picture language. In my spirit I saw a photographer's dark room with all the developing trays and that red dim light that they work with. I knew the Lord Jesus stood there as I was submerged in the developing liquid by His hands. I felt the Holy Spirit tell me that what I was going through was the Lord developing my character and spirit and that He would keep me there as long as it took for the image to sharpen to His satisfaction. I knew part of the process involved a 'pegging up' stage when the photograph is hung up to dry. Then I saw a framed photograph and everyone was admiring his work. I felt God tell me that there would be a process in which I would know His work in my life whilst in the dark room of sickness. There would be a second stage of 'waiting' whilst the process took place and a third stage would come when He would get the praise and glory as people agreed on His handiwork. I thanked God for this encouragement and looked forward to the time when people would be able to admire His work in me.

I had a scheduled ultrasound in the x-ray department of my local hospital on 14th June. I had decided to keep this even though I was awaiting the Basingstoke assessment. The diagnostic doctor told me that the tumour was now nearly one litre in density and had pushed my bladder over to the right so badly that I was not discharging all my urine, which meant that my ureter tubes were enlarged and had impacted my kidneys. She said she would need to speak to the consultant urgently. I told her about my pending assessment at The North Hampshire Hospital and she said she would pass this information on.

My gynaecologist was actually on holiday and I eventually saw him in clinic on 3rd July 2002. We talked about my options and he said he would be willing to admit me urgently, "But," he said, "I'll only be able to drain the tumour as it cannot be removed because it's part of your tissue." I mentioned my Basingstoke appointment and he told me he could see a copy of Mr. Moran's letter on my file. "I suppose you would be better going down there as they have all the expertise," he said, "but it's up to you to decide what you want to do." The choice was too hard for me, my dilemma was that I had got to wait until 5th August for my CT scan and assessment in Basingstoke and it was only 3rd July – I was wondering if my kidneys and bladder could last until then. I decided to ask him to contact Mr. Moran so that between them they could decide the best way forward. He said he would do this and telephone me.

Two days later I decided to write to Basingstoke myself, knowing my consultant's propensity to resist doing things at speed. I quickly typed a letter to Mr. Moran outlining my situation and managed to get it off in the Saturday morning post. Mid-morning on the Monday the telephone rang and I answered it without much thought. A soft Irish accent fell on my ears. "Hello, this is Mr. Moran, I received your letter today and I have telephoned your hospital to ask them not to intervene. I think you'll be okay until we can see you and it will be much better for you to have the one operation instead of several." He went on to explain why I had to wait until August; there were staff holidays delaying appointments. I thanked him for telephoning and without being able to think of anything useful to say, I said goodbye. I felt embarrassed at my lack of communication but at the same time very encouraged at his efficiency and kindness in speaking to me himself. I was glad I had been proactive for my own wellbeing.

Brian and I travelled the two hundred miles to Basingstoke on Sunday 4th August just two days before my 58th Birthday. We found the Travel Inn and ate our sandwiches and drove out to see where The North Hampshire Hospital was situated. We discovered a very nice park in the town so on the Monday morning we spent a pleasant few hours enjoying the sunshine and being together. I went into the ward at 2.00 p.m. and had the usual blood test and assessments. On the Tuesday (my birthday) I had the CT scan. Mr. Moran had been in the operating theatre all day and came to see us with the scan results at 7.00 p.m.

I was looking forward to seeing the owner of the lovely Irish voice that I had heard on the telephone a month previously. I imagined him very tall with aristocratic features. He was, in fact, of medium height, slim and very good looking. His manner matched his voice as he introduced himself to us with my scan film tucked under his arm. He showed us into a private room just off the ward and began to explain the scan details as he held them up to the light in the window, inviting us to *have a look*. I could see the large tumour filling my pelvis and my other organs struggling for a place in my abdomen. He began to explain the operation and how long it would take, and how long I would be in intensive care. 'It' would be a far bigger operation than I had had up until now, and "of course it will carry risks". He said I wasn't the worst 'Pseudo' case he had seen but he didn't pull any punches as he went on to talk about the particular risk of post operative blood clots. "We generally tell people," he continued "that there are three options for Pseudomyxoma Peritonei patients; a miracle, wait and see, or surgery". I knew my *wait and see* days had already come and gone, and as if reading my mind Brian said "We'll go for the surgery and expect miraculous things!"

"If you decide to go for the operation, and it sounds as if you will, you will need to be as fit as possible. Do you belong to a gym?" I nearly laughed out loud but I only smiled as I said "No, I didn't". "Well you ought to do some work on your cardiovascular system as the heart and lungs come under strain during the long hours of anaesthetic." I have always been a slim person and at 5' 7" never been overweight at all (apart from the tumours that added extra bulk). I explained I was used to walking the dog most days and thought I wasn't too bad. "Well we can all get fitter," he said in a kindly manner without making me feel stupid. He told me he would also prescribe vitamins and nutritional drinks and would be writing to my doctor to execute this arrangement. As I watched this lovely man making notes about me, I looked at his hands. Small slender fingers that had saved so many lives; would they save me also? As we left the room he shook our hands and touched both Brian and I on the shoulder that I took as a gesture of reassurance. This man had given me confidence and hope for the future.

Brian and I made our long trek home full of thankfulness to God that we had found someone who could help me.

It wasn't until a few days later that the Holy Spirit reminded me about the words He had given me months earlier. "The Best Man" had been one of them. Mr. Moran was at that time the only surgeon in the UK who was doing this operation and helping people with my condition. By this time I had read about Dr. Sugarbaker in Washington DC, USA, who had pioneered this surgery and I later learned that Mr. Moran had studied under him. As far as I knew then, the only other clinic of excellence for this disease was in Poland. I knew most definitely that God had provided "The Best Man" for my treatment and I was very grateful.

8

God's Sense of Humour

Just a day after our first visit to Basingstoke, I received a copy of the letter that Mr. Moran had sent to Professor Shepherd and my local doctors. He was offering me the surgery and suggesting that I start the nutrition and vitamin programme and that I book into a gymnasium and undertake an exercise routine under supervision.

There have been two things in life that I particularly feared and tried to avoid. I am not a good traveller in a car and hate most motorway journeys. They are too fast and furious for me. The best and quickest route from our home to Basingstoke after the A12 is M25,

M3 all the way! I have lost count now how many times I have had to get used to this route.

Also, I've never been a particularly shapely female, tall and slim, but rather straight up and down! Friends would mention about going to the gym and as I smiled and said "wonderful", my secret conversation with myself was "– okay for you – you look good – but you won't get me near those places". The picture I had of females in the gym was *brown, busty and beautiful,* and I was none of these things. Of course, I found out later that my preconceptions were completely groundless. So when I knew I had got to go, I was full of fear and completely intimidated.

I really did feel God was smiling at me saying "Now my child, conquer your fears and see how well you do with my enabling".

I paid my life membership fee at the local sport and leisure centre and the date was booked for my fitness assessment and initiation into the dreaded gym. The manager/supervisor person was tall, young and good looking – well he would be wouldn't he, just to add to my trepidation. However, he was very kind and exceedingly patient with this white, stick-like woman who could only manage the minimum of everything! Of course, my assessment revealed I was not very fit at all and my legs felt like jelly before ever starting the programme for real. He took me into the workout rooms and showed me how to use the equipment which was mostly digitally-controlled. I was a complete dunce at first as I carried around my programme card looking at each set of instructions. Why didn't other people have cards, they all looked so sure of what they were doing. I soon got used to everything and felt reasonably okay going on my own. It was hard work and I felt embarrassed because I looked 'not young' but my tumour made me look pregnant. However, I soon didn't care because this was going to help me get through the surgery and that was the main thing. It was interesting to meet some other people who were at the gym for medical reasons and I even got chatting with some of the "brown, busty and beautiful" girls and discovered that they were interested in my plight, saying encouraging comments like "You'll be fine, we will see you back here afterwards".

And so I had faced up to two more fears in my life and found that when God promises to be with us in every circumstance He means what He says.

The nutritional milk shakes that Mr. Moran prescribed were collected from the pharmacy with interest. "We hope you have got a car," said the assistant as she came out from behind the counter carrying two huge heavy bags with my name on the packages. Sixty in all were placed in the boot of the car with some embarrassment.

On Sunday 11th August, my daily Bible reading notes were based on Mark 6 v 50, the account of when Jesus came to his disciples when they were battling the storm. It had been an afternoon of great wonder as the disciples had helped Jesus to feed 5,000 people with just five bread rolls and a couple of small fish. As the day wore on, Jesus told his disciples to get in their boat and start out across the lake. He would make sure the people were dismissed in an orderly fashion. It turned out to be a very rough night as these tired disciples battled against a gale force wind and violent seas. It would seem that even these hardened fishermen were losing the fight against the elements and probably were fearing for their lives. In the middle of the night, Jesus came to them walking on the water. The Bible says that immediately Jesus got into the boat the storm died down. The notes read something like this: "Do you feel as if you're in a storm today? Like maybe you're not going to make it?" I was answering *Yes, Yes!* "When Jesus wants to teach us something He uses storms and adversities. It's during these times when we feel so separated from Him that He's actually teaching us the most. He doesn't show up early. Usually, He comes in the worst part of the storm just in the nick of time when you think you can't take any more. His presence alone should be enough for you in any storm. Be of good courage! The same Jesus who came to His disciples that night is with you now. You'll make it safely through! That's guaranteed!"

It felt as if the Holy Spirit was speaking to me personally but I still felt each day I waited for the surgery that I was on a roller coaster ride of feeling good and positive and then scared beyond reason. My journal for the 22nd August 2002 indicates that I felt like I was on a runaway train heading into a dark tunnel. I could not get off and even if I could the alternative was worse!

When I was at a low point, God would encourage me with something precious. One of these encouragements was: "When it feels as if all hell has broken loose in your life, remember Satan hasn't snatched the steering wheel from God. No, God's got it all worked out. Victory is born out of struggle." I was certainly struggling.

Jack, our very dear elderly neighbour, had died of cancer whilst I was in Basingstoke for my assessment on 6th August and the family, knowing Brian was a *religious leader person,* asked him to conduct the funeral service. Even though we were struggling with our own emotions, Brian did a wonderful job of making the crematorium service a friendly goodbye to their much loved family member. Hopefully we bore a good witness to our Lord and were able to display the comfort and love found in a compassionate and loving Saviour.

We are part of the 'dog walking fraternity' in our neck of the woods and Fern our lovely gentle Golden Retriever is well known by everyone. It was a great time to witness to people when they enquired after my health. I used to say, "Well if my faith in God doesn't hold good now it doesn't mean very much". It was interesting to watch responses. Most people like to think they believe in God but some find it difficult to talk about Him. I suppose some feel that a relationship with their Maker is a private thing and should not be talked of in such an open way. I found that many were sympathetic and willing to indulge me as they found some suitable response to my declaration of faith. I continue to hope that our *faith under fire* during those dark days made other people think deeper about their own relationship with a God who desires to help us.

9

The 'Mother of Them All'

Oswald Chambers says "the final thing is confidence in Jesus. Believe steadfastly in Him and all you come up against will develop your faith… Faith is unutterable trust in God which never dreams that He will not stand by us."

I had heard nothing further from Basingstoke hospital and we continued to keep life as normal as possible. I remember telling God how anxious I was about the surgery, and the Holy Spirit dropping a line from an old hymn into my heart 'The clouds you so much dread will break with blessing on your head'. I longed for the time of the blessing.

On 9th September the letter came. My operation was provisionally booked for 24th September 2002. They wanted me in on the Sunday and surgery would take place on the Tuesday. Brian and I began to prepare for our stay away from home. My sister, Jackie, and her husband had agreed to live in the house and look after our dog and two cats. There were several jobs to be done around the house and garden and we worked hard to leave everything in order, including stockpiling pet food and making lists of instructions for all eventualities. I was expected to be in hospital for twenty-eight days so we did everything we could in preparation for that.

One of the questions we had to address was Brian's accommodation whilst he was with me in Hampshire. About a month before my surgery, Brian went to a meeting in Norwich on behalf of our church. The speaker at that meeting told Brian that she lived in Basingstoke and would be happy to help with his accommodation. We had only spoken to Joanna once on the telephone previous to Brian meeting her and we thought perhaps she was just being polite in offering Brian accommodation, so we decided that it would probably be circumspect to not contact her regarding this. However, she sent an email and then telephoned reinforcing her offer and indicating that she would love to help as she lived only five minutes from the hospital. We decided to accept her kindness and as it turned out this was indeed God's wonderful provision for us. The North Hampshire Hospital is situated on the north side of Basingstoke between the main town centre and the small village of Sherborne St. John. Joanna and her husband Philip live in a very comfortable house in this village, which was indeed just a five-minute car journey from the hospital, and the distance could easily be managed on foot.

We arrived at Joanna and Philip's house in time to get Brian settled and unpacked before getting me into the hospital. Joanna and Philip were on holiday but their son met us and gave us keys and instructions. Brian would have the house to himself for a whole week before they returned. It proved to be a quiet place for him on the day I was operated on as he was able to sit in the garden in the warm late summer sunshine reading and praying during that long day.

I was admitted to a side room on the ward but the nurse said they couldn't guarantee I would remain there. I was glad of the personal toilet facilities. Part of preparation for this surgery entailed being 'pickle-axed' which basically is being emptied of every bit of food in the digestive system! I was also secretly glad that I would probably end up on the main ward as I wanted to know and meet other patients with my condition. Up until now I had not met anyone else with this horrible disease but I knew that as this was a centre for treating Pseudomyxoma Peritonei there must be other patients like me. I later learned that Mr. Moran and his team operated on one Pseudo patient each week because of the inevitable take up of an intensive care bed following each Pseudo surgery. We had been up since 4.00 a.m. and when Brian left me at 8.00 p.m. I was looking forward to going to sleep but then the senior house officer came in at 9.00 p.m. for preliminaries and questions. Soon after he left, the exhaustion of the day carried me away into my long awaited slumber.

Monday was very tiring as they continued to prepare me. Everything was explained: I would be in theatre at least eight hours and would wake up in intensive care with the ventilator still in place for a while in case more surgery had to be done. I would have a nasal gastric tube to flush out my stomach, four tubes in my abdomen where further chemo would be administered, as well as the surgical drain. Two ureteric stents would be inserted into the ureters to give stability during the long hours of surgery. An ileostomy stoma would be opened on my right side and a catheter would be in place. Pain would be controlled initially by an epidural in the spine. I was given the usual ECG to check my heart, and a chest x-ray and bloods taken. They said I would be required for the theatre by 7.15 a.m. the next morning.

By the time it came for Brian to leave I was very tearful. If anything went wrong with the surgery this would be the last time we would hold each other. I regretted being upset because it made things harder for him. He was gone and I felt very scared and alone but within a few minutes a nurse stood in the doorway with the telephone, "You have a call – a lady named Jill" Jill was a child protection manager for whom I had worked at Suffolk's Social Services Department. We had spent many hours working and travelling together to various meetings. Jill is one of those interesting people who is always full of cheerfulness and huge amounts of internal energy. She used to ask me questions about my faith and she always respected what I believed even if she disagreed. She is one of the few feminists that I have met who I truly like. She knew I was in Basingstoke Hospital and had taken the trouble to find the telephone number, intending to leave me a message at the nurses' station. When they said she could speak to me she was delighted and so was I. I believe God arranges such divine blessings as He knew the one person who could really cheer me up and make me laugh at that particular time when I was feeling so dreadful. Her energetic banter and real concern for me was just what I needed.

As I said cheerio to her and gave the phone back to the nurse, Mr. Moran appeared in the doorway. "I've just come to see if you are alright for tomorrow," he said in his lovely Irish accent, as if he were talking about a visit to the shops or some everyday outing. He smiled as I replied in the affirmative. "You'll be fine – see you tomorrow then," he said as he turned to go on his way. I wondered about his wife and children and how they must be used to doing without him so much. I felt much better so I took myself off for a hot bath and after such a tiring day I fell asleep without much difficulty.

I was woken up early the next morning. I washed and got into the theatre gown, got into the prepared bed, took my pre-med and tried to doze. I remember being wheeled down to the operating room and the wonderful anaesthetist waiting for me. He had visited me the day previously with such reassurance, "I will keep you alive, no need to worry; and I will wake you up just at the right time" I believed him!

I woke up in the evening in intensive care, still with the ventilator in my throat. They took it out at some point because I remember talking to the nurse in the middle of the night. There were a lot of people around me. I found out later that I had lost two litres of blood during the operation and my low blood pressure was causing concern. I heard them call for the doctor and as he stood with his back to me I heard him say, "If she becomes tachy-cardic call me directly". I was frightened and called out that I wished someone would talk to me. Sister bent over me and said they were going to give me some blood and they could fix things for me. In my morphine stupor I asked for them to get Brian because he would pray for me. Sister told me it was two o'clock in the morning and I remember saying to her that Brian wouldn't mind coming, and then I fell asleep again into carefree oblivion. They did indeed have to give me two litres of blood before my status began to improve.

It was not until many days later as Brian was taking me home that he told me that he had caused quite a stir when he visited me in the intensive care unit. He had occupied himself all day by reading and praying and had eaten just soup and bread rolls. When he came in to see me for the first time he bent down to kiss me and passed out, collapsing on the floor beside me! I remember him squeezing my hand but my immediate loss of consciousness again saved me from sharing his embarrassment. He told me that doctors and nurses rushed to his aid; plying him with water and digestive biscuits. They tested his blood sugar levels but they were okay. He was made to lie down in the rest room and advised not to drive, as it could happen again. We laughed about it afterwards and decided it must have been due to anxiety.

My recovery was good and I was soon taken to the high dependency unit for twenty-four hours, then into a four-bed ward where I met other 'Pseudo' patients recovering from surgery. Every stage is a milestone when recovering from surgery and things like coming off intravenous painkillers, having this drain out and then that one, are all big steps in your fragile world. All kinds of medications were administered via the main line in my neck which felt to me like lace-making bobbins dangling and tinkling each time the nurses used them. I had been told that at the end of the operation one surgeon stands for approximately one-hour administering the heated liquid chemo into the abdomen. It is done very carefully and slowly as it is rolled around each organ in turn before closing up the abdomen. This was supplemented by three further lots of liquid chemo being administered directly into my abdomen on three following days. Each day this liquid was dripped into the cavity of the abdomen they would move me from side to side to ensure the chemo reached all parts of the intestines and other organs. This, hopefully, would attack any residual tiny deposits of the Pseudo material. I had two treatments subsequent to the operation but the drains in me leaked, soaking both me and the bed covers. Mr. Moran decided to scrap the third dose in my case.

They fed me intravenously for many days by Total Parenteral Nutrition (TPN) which is a special milky nutritional formula fed through the main line in the neck. The 'lace bobbins' were indeed very useful! These wonderful tailor-made food bags are very costly and I was very grateful that they were all part of the fabulous care that I received courtesy of the National Health Service. The nasal gastric tube was soon removed and I was heartily pleased to have my nose back to normal and my throat free. The catheter came out as soon as walking to the toilet could be accomplished. I had been told to expect to have another stoma so the ileostomy bag was not so shocking to me as I'd learned to cope with a colostomy the year previously. Apparently I was a unique Pseudo patient, having had both a colostomy and an ileostomy. It brought me no sense of pride at all. The ileostomy would be reversed and the temporary inconvenience was a small price to pay for getting this treatment. Another small price paid was I no longer had a *belly button* as it had disappeared under the scalpel.

The first visit by Mr. Moran and his team after the surgery was so encouraging for me. He said that they had managed to remove all the tumour, and with the chemo my outlook was good. They were very pleased with how things had gone. In fact, the eight-hour operation for me was a 'short day' in surgery for the team as many Pseudo operations take twelve hours and more. The team laughed as they confirmed that they were able to get an early supper.

Each day this marvellous band of consultants and doctors would visit and apply their expertise to my situation. "Yes, the drain can come out, yes start her on fluids, yes she needs an antibiotic for that infection, etc." I fell in love with them all!

Visitors were allowed into the hospital ward at ten o'clock in the morning. Our rest period was from twelve-thirty until two in the afternoon, when visitors could return until eight in the evening. Each day Brian would arrive with his smiling face, he would kiss me and I would bring him up to date on the 'horrors' and the 'delights' of hospital life. He usually arrived when I was being washed and in the early days he would wash my feet and legs, run my little battery shaver over my now hedgehog like legs and then apply moisturiser. I was the envy of the ward.

One day as Brian sat by my bed, a couple walked in and began a conversation with us. I thought at first they were visitors for another patient but we soon discovered that the man had had a Pseudo operation just six weeks previously. This was his follow-up appointment day in clinic and he had come up onto the ward to encourage recovering Pseudo patients. "The man's a saint," he said, singing Mr. Moran's praises. "Just look at me" – and I was. He was about fortyish and very tall and slim. "I was bloated out here," he continued, putting his hands where his big stomach had once been, "but he's fixed me!" As we agreed that he did indeed look the picture of health we asked where they were from because their accent sounded very familiar. They were from Gorleston, Norfolk, just eight miles up the road from us and living in the town where our church fellowship was and where we had worked and ministered for a number of years. It suddenly dawned on me that this man would have been seen at the same local hospital as myself so I asked him who his consultant was and how he got a referral to Mr. Moran. He had, in fact, been diagnosed and referred directly from our local hospital. Of course, he had seen a different consultant to me but still it left me wondering about the anomalies in communication in the same hospital that left me having to find out about the Basingstoke Centre for myself and having to work so hard for a referral.

Brian's accommodation whilst I was in hospital was a small miracle in itself, and a wonderful example of how God provides for his children. These two dear Christian people have been so generous to us and have continued to allow us to stay in their home whenever I have had to return for clinic appointments. Without any cost to us they have showed us loving kindness and I honour them both for their trust in us. Their beautiful home has been a haven for us after long journeys into Hampshire.

During my stay in Basingstoke Hospital, Brian discovered that Ron Trudinger, the Christian teacher and author of many books including *'Built to Last'* and *'Cells for Life'*, was also an in-patient. He was, by this time, a very elderly and frail gentleman. Ron's wife, Sue, was a friend and colleague of Joanna and attended the same church. Brian was able to visit Ron on his ward and pray with him which was a great encouragement to this ageing Christian. Brian was by chance re-reading *'Built to Last'* and had it under his arm when he visited this dear man. Although Ron was very ill, he was so delighted to see *his* book in Brian's hand. Whenever Brian began to share a verse of Scripture with him, he would join in and complete the whole verse accurately and with obvious faith. Ron Trudinger died on 28th October 2002 and went to be with his Lord.

Brian brought me home after three weeks. The two-hundred mile journey was very hard but each hour brought me nearer to my beloved home and familiar surroundings. I had made it by the Grace of God and a great deal of help from a lot of people, and outstanding medical skill.

10

FORGIVENESS

Apart from returning to The North Hampshire Hospital on 7th November 2002 for a day when I was seen in clinic and had my ureteric stents removed (not a nice experience), the latter months of that year were quiet as I recovered at home. My two sisters were wonderful, coming in to clean, shop and to do the laundry.

During one of these quiet days, Brian and I watched a video of R. T. Kendal preaching on total forgiveness. His whole sermon was based on the Old Testament character of Joseph, who had been sold into Egypt by his brothers, and his subsequent total forgiveness of them and their wickedness. Joseph suffered greatly in a foreign country because of what his jealous brothers did to him. He lost his freedom and was wrongly accused and imprisoned for years. Joseph maintained faith and integrity and eventually became the most important ruler in Egypt, second only to Pharaoh. Joseph's courage and bravery saved Egypt and the surrounding countries from famine and death. When his brothers turned up in Egypt requesting to buy food from him he could have exacted full revenge for their treatment of him years earlier. After all, Joseph had all the power and authority now to order their deaths or at the very least send them away without food. The Bible story tells us that instead of revenge, Joseph freely forgave them and showed them mercy.

I was challenged by his words and reflected on whether I was holding on to any unforgiveness in my own spirit. I could not think of anyone against whom I was unforgiving. I smugly commended myself for not 'harbouring a grudge' against anyone I knew. Oh how deceitful our hearts can be at times, and how little we really know ourselves. A couple of days later a friend telephoned to enquire about my progress and as I brought her up to date she asked how my referral to the Basingstoke Centre came about. I found myself reiterating my disappointment and anger at what I felt was the local consultant's lack of interest in my condition and what I perceived as his negligence. I relished telling her about how I thought my GP had been inefficient and uncaring, as she made the suitable empathetic noises. She wished me well and we said goodbye.

The next day the Holy Spirit reminded me about R. T. Kendal's sermon and the many times I had prayed "forgive us our sins, as we forgive those who sin against us". I felt God's light shining in my dark heart, as I realised that each time I criticised these men – and I had done this often – it was evidence of my unforgiving heart. I told God I was sorry and ashamed that I had been so smug. As I repented I thanked God for the care and help that these medical professionals had given me and I promised that I would not repeat any details again to anyone. Then I remembered that the manuscript for this book contained an account of my anger and disappointment because I thought they were less than proactive in finding the right help for me. I made the necessary adjustments because I want to truly honour my local consultant and GP for their skill and help in treating me. Sometimes when we are under pressure our thinking is selfish and defensive and full of biased opinions, which was the case with me. I have since asked God to forgive me for my selfish criticism and it is of no matter whether I was right or wrong to think the way I did. God made sure I was given the very best treatment in the end and I am eternally grateful.

Oswald Chambers says that the entrance into the Kingdom is through the *panging pains of repentance crashing into a man's respectable goodness*. I know this probably refers to the initial time when the light first shines into the human heart revealing that respectable goodness is not enough, but it is also true for people who have been Christians a long time. *Panging pains of repentance* need to be a lifelong habit, allowing the Holy Spirit to make us like our Saviour. God's intention, once He has drawn us to Himself, is to make us like His Son who said "Father forgive them for they know not what they do".

The old Puritans used to pray for "the gift of tears". How little we know of this in this modern society of brashness and self realisation; of elbowing to be the winner with no shame for our stupidity and lack of love, kindness and generous spirit for others. As long as we rake over old grievances and rehearse old injuries, we are not practising total forgiveness.

When Joseph met his brothers after those long years, he protected them from others being aware of their sin against him. Joseph sent all the servants and officials out of the room as he made himself known to his brothers. What a man he was to be able to say "You meant it for harm, but God meant it for good!"

If we believe in a Sovereign God who allows and engineers our circumstances then we have to say with Joseph, "It looked like harm to me, but God meant it for my good and the good of others". When 'bad' things happen to us, our response should be unutterable trust in our Heavenly Father.

I have found tremendous freedom when I have been prepared to let my un-forgiveness go. In return, the Holy

Spirit has given me positive feelings for those I felt had wronged me, and God has even helped me to pray for them. Sometimes we have been hurt so badly by people that it takes on-going effort to get through to a place of freedom. If we tell God we want to feel differently and pray a blessing on the people who we find it difficult to forgive, then gradually we will be able to be free. Obey the Holy Spirit and your feelings will change. Don't wait to feel differently before you pray for those who have wronged you. Repent of your unforgiveness and then pray for the person.

11

DÉJÀ VU

I thought the early months of 2003 were difficult; little did I know that the pressure would increase even more. Whilst I was waiting for my admission date for the ileostomy to be reversed, we had bad news about our beautiful dog Fern. We took her to the vet for teeth de-scaling and an x-ray as she was rather overweight and had been vomiting. They rang us whilst she was in surgery saying that she had tumours and the spleen would have to be removed, asking if we wanted them to proceed, or not to wake her up again. We were heartbroken but clear in our minds that we wanted her home for however long we had with her.

My admission date for going to Basingstoke came through for third February. As we prepared to go, handing our dog's recovery over to my long suffering sister, heavy snow fell. My fears piled up – along with the snow – for my dog, my surgery and the dangerous driving conditions for our trip into Hampshire. As it turned out, the day we travelled was very sunny and as we left East Anglia behind the snow became less of a problem. I was thankful and relieved.

The reversal surgery took place as scheduled but I forgot to tell the nursing staff that I was intolerant to a certain antibiotic, which, of course, was the exact one they gave me. However, I recovered and Brian took me home after a week's stay.

It's very easy to write a couple of sentences about this less major surgery, dismissing it quickly as another little episode in my life. The details, however, hang around in my memory like some awful clinging cobweb. Like the day when the ward was full of visitors and I mistakenly thought I needed to pass wind. The subsequent clean up operation was just another embarrassing episode that is best left without description or elucidation.

We were both glad to get home again and discover that our old dog was doing well. Although I tried very hard to get back into normal routine, I felt unwell and tired. My intestines were not working well and in March I began to have pain and colic and many episodes of early morning vomiting.

Despite several visits to the GP, two visits to our local Accident and Emergency Department, an outpatient appointment at The North Hampshire Hospital in Basingstoke, and a week's admission on the ward at our local hospital, my condition continued to deteriorate and the vomiting worsened. I lost weight and could eat only small amounts of food. My local hospital had indicated that I did not have an obstruction but a 'hold-up' somewhere inside my intestines.

We were becoming desperate as my body began to shut down. I dreaded leaving my home again but we knew something was very wrong and we needed to act quickly. On Sunday 1st June 2003 Brian drove me down to Hampshire again with the intention of presenting ourselves at Basingstoke Hospital's Accident and Emergency Department. We arrived at ten o'clock in the morning and were treated with kindness and concern. Although we waited for most of the day, I was eventually admitted to the ward. Our very kind friends readily agreed for Brian to stay at their house again.

I spent a week on intravenous feeding (TPN) because I was so malnourished. They gave me a CT scan and a colonoscopy. The medical staff were brilliant and assured me that they could *sort me out*. Although the CT scan was not very definitive the doctors said they clearly had to operate to discover what was happening internally. I underwent my fourth laparotomy on 11th June and they discovered that I had probably had a small leak following either from the stoma reversal in February, or from the original major surgery in 2002. An abscess had formed in my pelvis which had caused an obstruction in the small bowel. I was in theatre three hours and woke up in the recovery room where I remained all night because I intermittently stopped breathing. I recall a very lovely Filipino nurse calling my name every time I went off to sleep and forgot to breath. She stayed with me all night long and I am thankful for her lovely face and thorough care.

And so I spent the next two weeks recovering again from major surgery; and eventually my time came to go home. Brian had once again been my patient, loving husband who never moaned about his own disjointed circumstances. Driving two hundred miles was again an ordeal but we were glad to be making our way home and to all that we loved. I could eat again and we talked about going out together to our favourite eating places.

Fern was in the driveway as we parked the car and it took her a few moments to realise who we were. I am sure she had forgotten her relationship with us until she made some connection in her doggy brain that we actually lived in this place and belonged to her. I fell on my knees in the garden and quietly wept. The flowers were in bloom – it was 21st June – and I was home.

There were many people who God sent my way during those three awful weeks. I will mention just one miracle of his love and concern for me. Bruce came to visit me during the first week of my admission. Bruce is a Christian who lives in Basingstoke and he had heard about me from our friends Joanna and Philip with whom Brian had stayed. Bruce took it upon himself to minister in the hospital and he came several times to pray with me. On one visit he said "It's a pity my friend John is not here to pray with you, he would know what to say and he's had great success in praying for healing". Although I was very depressed and extremely weak, I managed to show some enthusiasm by replying "Oh it would be lovely if he could come". "Well," Bruce replied, "he lives in Birmingham so it's unlikely."

Bruce told me later that when he left the hospital he sent a text message to John with one question; "Where are you?" The reply came back "I'm in Basingstoke for a couple of days before I pick my wife up from Gatwick Airport". Bruce said later that he was astonished and quickly arranged to meet John and bring him to see me.

They came and prayed and ministered. I cried and confessed my sin and need for Jesus to give me peace and healing. John said that the Lord had spoken to him about me and that I had allowed stress to overtake me and crush me. We talked about my stressful job in the local county council office and they prayed that I would know peace and healing. John prophecised that instead of the tears, God would fill my mouth with laughter. That I was not to fear as the Lord would fight for me. Bruce read a Bible verse to me from 1 Thessalonians 1 v. 4 and said that God not only loved me but had put his hand upon me for service.

What sweet and generous men of God they were. How grateful I am for their loving kindness to me. What a wonderful God who sovereignly planned for this man to collect his wife from Gatwick airport at just the time I was in need of his ministry in Basingstoke.

They did me good and their prophetic words were encouraging and enabling. I did, indeed, learn to laugh again but it took time.

12

FERN

Fern is a Golden Retriever who never turned golden. Her coat has remained blonde throughout her life. Her pedigree name is Starmas and her father's name was Fen Boy and her mother was Pretty Blondie. We do not know what she was like in the litter but throughout her life she has been a complex mixture of gentleness and stubbornness. She came into our lives when she was just twelve months old when the family with whom she had lived could no longer keep her. There were four children in the family and Fern missed them terribly when she came to our quiet, child-free home.

Her first year with us caused us many problems. I vacuumed the carpets so much because of her white dog hairs being everywhere that I developed tennis elbow. She was *wild* to begin with and a harmless game with her would soon turn into ferocious snarling. We cured that with a water pistol! She would pull items off the washing line and rip them to pieces. If we were out walking and we came across a family with a picnic, like lightening she would be in there stealing anything edible. Many times we have been sworn at because of our manic dog.

She has always loved water – as most Retrievers do. She was unable to discriminate between clean and dirty. Every ditch, pond and stream had her name on it. Many times we have travelled home in the car with her stinking so badly that we hardly dare breathe. Sometimes we had to make a detour to the sea shore so a further swim in the sea would wash away most of the dirt.

One of her favourite places used to be a lovely pinewood backing onto the Norfolk Broads. She would leap two-foot into the air as she escaped the confines of the car as we arrived. She would scamper off to chase rabbits, returning to us when she thought appropriate. If she found an oily black puddle before we got to the water she would make sure her under belly was suitably cooled, laying full length in the terrible mess. Passing walkers would gasp as she returned to us looking like a hillside sheep; white top and black underbelly and legs. Many times we lost her in those woods but she always managed to find her way back to the car park.

Only those who have owned a dog will appreciate these anecdotes. Apologies to the readers who know nothing of poopy-scoops, dog breath, dirty paw marks and doggy hairs in the car upholstery, to say nothing of the rain-soaked days when walking the dog is no pleasure. We were quite unused to 'the dog world' before we had her but of course you have to learn quickly. Much like becoming a parent for the first time.

There is a joke about a cat and a dog sitting in front of a blazing fire, both staring reflectively into the flames. The silence is broken by the cat saying "I think cats are more intelligent than dogs, don't you?" There is a pregnant pause before the dog replies "What's a dog?"!

I like that silly story because dogs often do really stupid things. Fern is no exception. However, she is often quite a 'knowing' creature and has reminded me of many spiritual lessons.

When Fern was younger and very playful, we used to play a game with her that involved us pretending we could not see her. We would look out of the window and the door and call her name. We would look at each other and ask "Where is she?" Whilst all this crescendo was building she was at our feet trying to let us know that she was there and that we were very stupid not to see her. When she could stand it no longer she barked at us, and we clapped our hands because we had *found her* again; and everyone enjoyed the reunion. (I have to mention that on one occasion when playing this game, we became aware that the neighbours had been watching and listening. Our credibility took a nose dive.)

It always reminds me of the truth that we Christians affirm that God is always with us; and He is of course. However, when things get difficult we start to say "Well where is He? I can't see the evidence of His presence." We know the truth but we play games and only recognise the reality of his presence when we feel better and all is well.

Dogs are creatures of habit and usually their meals come at the same time each day. When it's time for Fern's meal she finds a place in the room where I'm working and so begins the 'watch'. Her eyes follow me around the room. Her head remains still but her black eyes take in my every move. She moves only when her cupboard opens and her food comes out. It reminds me of Psalm 123 v. 2. "As the eyes of slaves look to the hand of their master, as the eyes of a maid look to the hand of her mistress, so our eyes look to the Lord our God till He shows us his mercy".

Fern loves my sister and brother-in-law, as they have looked after her so many times when I have been in hospital. When they are calling to see me, I tell Fern "Jackie and Richard are coming". She sits at the gate waiting and waiting and if they are delayed she gets disappointed and disillusioned. She comes into the house and finds me, staring into my face for answers. I am reminded that our Lord has told us that He will come back to this earth again.

We look for Him – especially when life is unbearable – and we become disillusioned. Fern's delight when her favourite friends arrive is clear to all as she dances back and forth enjoying the fulfilled promises of love and attention. Jesus will come again, as He has promised, and our delight will also cause us to dance with the reality of His presence.

Fern has had her health problems and strangely enough they have mirrored my own condition. She, too, has had tumours in her abdomen necessitating surgery. When her spleen was removed, the vet said she had only a short while to live, but the subsequent histology could not confirm malignancy and she has survived together with me. I have prayed over her, asking the Lord to give her to us as long as He ordains. She reminds me of myself; fragile but surviving by the grace of our God.

Dogs can be hard work but we love her dearly and dread the day of her departure. There is nothing in the Bible to say that animals go to heaven. However, my Saviour says He will "restore all things". That's good enough for me – and Fern.

13

A Fence of Feathers

God has been gracious to me and allowed me to live – but I shall die at some time. Meanwhile, I have learned to live within the limitations which multiple surgery has left me with.

My prayer is that I will never take for granted the joy of life, the smell and sight of spring flowers, the simple joy of walking out with Brian, and (and I never thought I would say this) being able to do my own grocery shopping. The privilege of being able to attend church and worship with others remains a great delight. So many of our congregation have supported and loved us through our difficult and overwhelming days, and we appreciate them all.

In August 2004 I celebrated my sixtieth birthday and in the same month Brian and I had open house when friends and family came to celebrate with us our Ruby Wedding Anniversary. My annual CT scans continue at The North Hampshire Hospital in Basingstoke and each year we look to God for good results.

When we arrive in the eternal courts of heaven, I am pretty sure all our questions about suffering in this world will die on our lips. There are so many questions. My ordeal was huge to me and my loved ones, but still small compared to what some dear people have to endure. What about the children? What about the chronic and permanently disabled? The questions are as old as the human race and were no less poignant when asked by Job in the Old Testament all those many years ago when his health failed and his faith was severely tested. For me, my own peace comes out of knowing that for reasons not known by us, God allows this broken world to continue in its fallen state for the time being. I am convinced that God allows this 'bundle of life' to shape our characters so that we prefer to trust Him rather than blame Him.

I am thinking, too, that pain is not always physical and that some people who flourish in their health suffer in other ways. It is not just our bodies that bend under the weight of life and circumstances. I am reminded of those who stand tall whilst the savage winds of grief blow away their two teenage children in one day. Of the woman who continues to draw from the well of God's love even though she is stuck in a loveless marriage. I know a young couple whose faith remained alive when the machine was switched off that was keeping their seventeen-hour-old baby son alive. What of the pain of husbands and wives who have to watch as their once beautiful son destroys his life through ugly addictions.

As I look back over my life I salute those who I have known who have borne their not so obvious pain with dignity and courage. History is littered with individuals who refused to be small in the face of overwhelming pain and suffering. I want to belong to this army of giants who will finish life well. We always have a choice. We can blame Him or Trust Him.

And when the time comes, the glory that we will receive and enjoy will chase away all memory of the pain and the answers will no longer be necessary, for He has promised to wipe away all tears from our eyes. The Apostle Paul said "this light affliction is not worthy to be compared with the eternal weight of glory" which we will experience.

Since reading about the life and work of Amy Carmichael many years ago, I have admired and loved her. Although a vigorous and courageous young missionary in India during the last century, she had a serious accident in 1931 and was more and more confined to her room. Her body knew great pain and frustrating limitation but her mind and spirit remained active and passionate for God. She died in 1951, having rescued hundreds of women and children from physical and often moral danger. The

Dohnavur Fellowship that she founded exists to this day in south India. If she had remained physically able, it is unlikely she would have been so prolific in her writings that I, and many others, have benefited from since.

Amy Carmichael has described the limitations of suffering and pain as a "fence of feathers" ("*with His feathers has He made a fence for thee*" a rendering of Psalm 91 v. 4). In a letter she wrote to someone who had just had an operation she says "Nestle under those feathers, and when you are tempted to press against the fence, remember it is a fence of feathers – soft and downy, and yet strong as the feathers of great birds are. May those feathers be very comforting to you through these days."

Our God never preferred suffering but since we exist for the time being in this fallen world, our Father allows us the privilege and honour of glorifying Him in it.

My Prayer

Father, thank you for the person who is reading these words. You know all their circumstances and difficulties and so I pray that you will reveal your amazing love and generosity to them that they may understand and grasp how much you want a relationship with them.

Thank you for your son, Jesus, who died on the cross so that we could be forgiven and have that relationship with you. We know we need you because we cannot make it through life – and death – on our own. Therefore, we put our trust in you, the living God.

Your son, Jesus, said "Come to me, all of you who are weary and carry heavy burdens, and I will give you rest"*. Your invitation gives us hope and we bow our heads and hold out our hands to you, praying that we may know for ourselves the peace that you have promised.

Amen

* *(St. Matthews's Gospel, Chapter 11 and Verse 28: New Living translation)*

References

1. Oswald Chambers, *My Utmost for His Highest,* p.viii
2. Amy Carmichael, *Rose from Brier,* p.22
3. *Christian Witness to Israel,* Summer Bulletin 2001, p.25
4. John S. Ross, *Faith Hanging by a Thread,* p.25
5. *United Christian Broadcasting Notes,* 11th August 2002, p.42
6. Amy Carmichael, *Candles in the Dark,* p.75